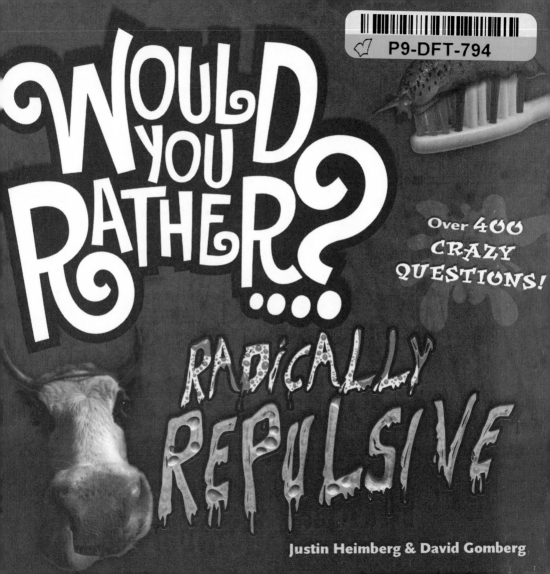

Would You Rather...?

Radically Repulsive

Over 400 CRAZY QUESTIONS!

Justin Heimberg & David Gomberg

Published by Seven Footer Press
247 West 30th, Second Floor
New York, NY 10001

Scholastic Edition, November 2010
10 9 8 7 6
Grand Rapids, Michigan June 2011

Design by Thomas Schirtz

ISBN 978-1-934734-41-4

www.sevenfooterpress.com

Table of Contents

HOW TO USE THIS BOOK

1. Sit around with a bunch of friends.
2. Read a question from the book out loud and talk about it.

   You won't believe some of the stuff you'll come up with as you think about which choice to make.
3. Everybody must choose! That's the whole point. It forces you to really think about the options.
4. Once everyone has chosen, move on to the next question.

It's that simple. We have provided a few things to think about for each question, but don't stop there. Much of the fun comes from imagining the different ways your choice will affect your life. Don't hold back as you discuss the options. Be silly, gross, and funny. There are no wrong answers, although some people might consider the questions themselves to be very very "wrong." Enough jibber-jabber. It's time to enter the demented world of *Would You Rather...?*.

CHAPTER ONE

1

Repulsive

There are a lot of words that mean "gross" that start with the letter "R." "Revolting." "Repugnant." "Repulsive." There are also words that begin with the letter "R" that mean cool: "Remarkable," "Resplendent," "Radical". Well, we say things can be both cool and disgusting, so why not throw those words together. With that in mind, enjoy these questions that range from the "Remarkably Revolting" to the "Resplendently Repulsive." Oh, and one more "R" word describes these questions: Ridiculous.

Would you rather...

have a beetle crawl in and around your mouth for 2 minutes

OR

have an inch worm slowly inch up your left nostril and out your right nostril?

Would you rather...

have a tongue made of hair

OR

have hair made of tongues?

YOU MUST CHOOSE!

WOULD YOU RATHER...LICK ALL THE DEAD BUGS OFF THE FRONT OF A CAR WINDSHIELD

OR DRINK A GLASS OF SWEAT WRUNG OUT OF USED UNDERWEAR AFTER A PROFESSIONAL BASKETBALL TEAM'S PRACTICE?

Would you rather live in a world where...

it rains mayonnaise

OR

where it snows slugs?

After making your choice, think of all the ways your life would be different. Would you go outside on a rainy day and hold out your bologna sandwich? Would you have a slug-ball fight? How hard would it be to shovel sticky slugs off your driveway?

YOU MUST CHOOSE!

Would you rather...

have zits that pop by themselves, squirting as much goo as there is in a ketchup packet

OR

have zits that crawl all over your face like little ants?

Would you rather...

have living boogers that fly out of your nose and buzz around like bees

OR

have glow-in-the-dark poop?

Things to think about: creating a nightlight outside your tent when camping, boogers landing in people's hair

Would you rather...

eat a handful of chocolate-covered cockroaches

OR

a plate of deep-fried roadkill?

Would you rather...

get hit in the face with a soggy spit ball the size of a basketball

OR

get hit in the face with a "yellow snowball"?

Would you rather...

feel compelled to greet people by licking their feet

OR

by intensely smelling their armpits?

Would you rather...

have never-ending hiccups

OR

never-ending gas?

Things to think about: sleeping, elevators, giving book reports and speeches

Would you rather...

have your backpack always full of rocks

OR

always full of fish heads?

Things to think about: smelly books, walking to school, reaching into your bag to get a pencil at the bottom

Would you rather...

have every dog you pass find your leg an irresistible place to pee

OR

every bird you pass find your hair an irresistible place to poop?

WOULD YOU RATHER...EAT AN EARWAX BURRITO

OR SUCK ON A DROOL-SICLE?

Would you rather...

get poison ivy under your eyelid

OR

on your tongue?

Where would be the worst place to get poison ivy? Can you imagine a plant where if you touch it, it does something silly to you like turns you purple or makes your skin into corduroy? Invent your own plant!

YOU MUST CHOOSE!

Would you rather...

be yawning and have eight moths fly into your mouth

OR

just one mosquito?

Would you rather...

eat cat food for two weeks

OR

one heaping spoonful of your friends' boogers?

Would you rather...

find a used Band-Aid in your sloppy joe

OR

put on your underwear only to realize someone had filled it with sloppy joe?

Would you rather eat a 'sloppy joe' or a 'neat joe'?

Would you rather...

have each hair on your body suddenly turn into a flea

OR

have your saliva suddenly turn into glue?

Things to think about: your mouth getting stuck shut, swallowing, spitting, rubbing your fleas on someone you hate, using bug spray as deodorant

YOU MUST CHOOSE!

Would you rather...

fart loudly with every step your right foot takes

OR

belch every time you breathe out?

Things to think about: holding your breath, going to a dance, hopping on one foot (but imagine the gassy build-up when that right foot finally comes down!)

Would you rather...

throw up right into a fan

OR

throw up at the peak of a trampoline bounce and land in it, bouncing in it five times?

YOU MUST CHOOSE!

Would you rather...

drink a glass of ten-month-old-milkshake complete with green chunky goodness

OR

eat a bowl of rat tails 'n cheese?

Would you rather...

get a Purple Nurple from your grandma

OR

an Indian Burn from your grandpa?

Would you rather...

have blue fungus grow on your hands

OR

black mold grow on your teeth?

Would you rather...

have to wear the same underwear for two weeks straight

OR

have to wear the same pair of socks for two months straight?

Things to think about: At the end, what would you do with the underwear or socks? Give them to charity or would that be cruel? Raise them in pride on the flagpole? Burn them and watch the horrible spirits emerge from the smoldering smelly fabric?

WOULD YOU RATHER...EAT COTTON CANDY THAT TURNED OUT TO BE A COCOON FULL OF CATERPILLARS
CRUNCH!
CHEW!

OR SPIKE A VOLLEYBALL ONLY TO REALIZE IT WAS A WASP NEST?
SWARM!

Would you rather...

use bug-gut toothpaste

OR

use horse-manure-scented soap?

Would you rather...

jump off a diving board into a pool of cow slobber **OR** glue?

chocolate Magic Shell **OR** root beer?

camel spit **OR** garbage?

Would you rather...

use a live possum as a pillow each night

OR

use a pile of rolled-up dirty diapers?

Would you rather...

have to share toothbrushes with (think of the grossest person you know)

OR

switch underwear with (insert someone almost as gross)?

Authors' Debate

Would you rather...

vomit marbles

"I'd lose my marbles." – Justin Heimberg

When you sweat cheese, remember we're talking about your whole body: under your arms, behind your knees, every nook and cranny. Vomiting marbles would be a little painful, sure, but at least it's clean. Imagine how cool the sound of the marbles hitting the floor would be. And then you have something to do to kill time: a nice game of stomach juice-covered marbles. If used right, marble vomit can even be an effective self-defense weapon.

YOU MUST CHOOSE!

OR sweat cheese?

"Cheese, Please!" – David Gomberg

Sweating cheese is a good thing. You'd never have to buy food again. Anytime you are hungry, just build up a sweat. Just carry some crackers in your pocket. Throwing up liquid is bad enough. Imagine a bunch of hard spheres being violently summoned from your stomach, up through your throat and out your mouth, beating up the back of your teeth like regurgitated bullets.

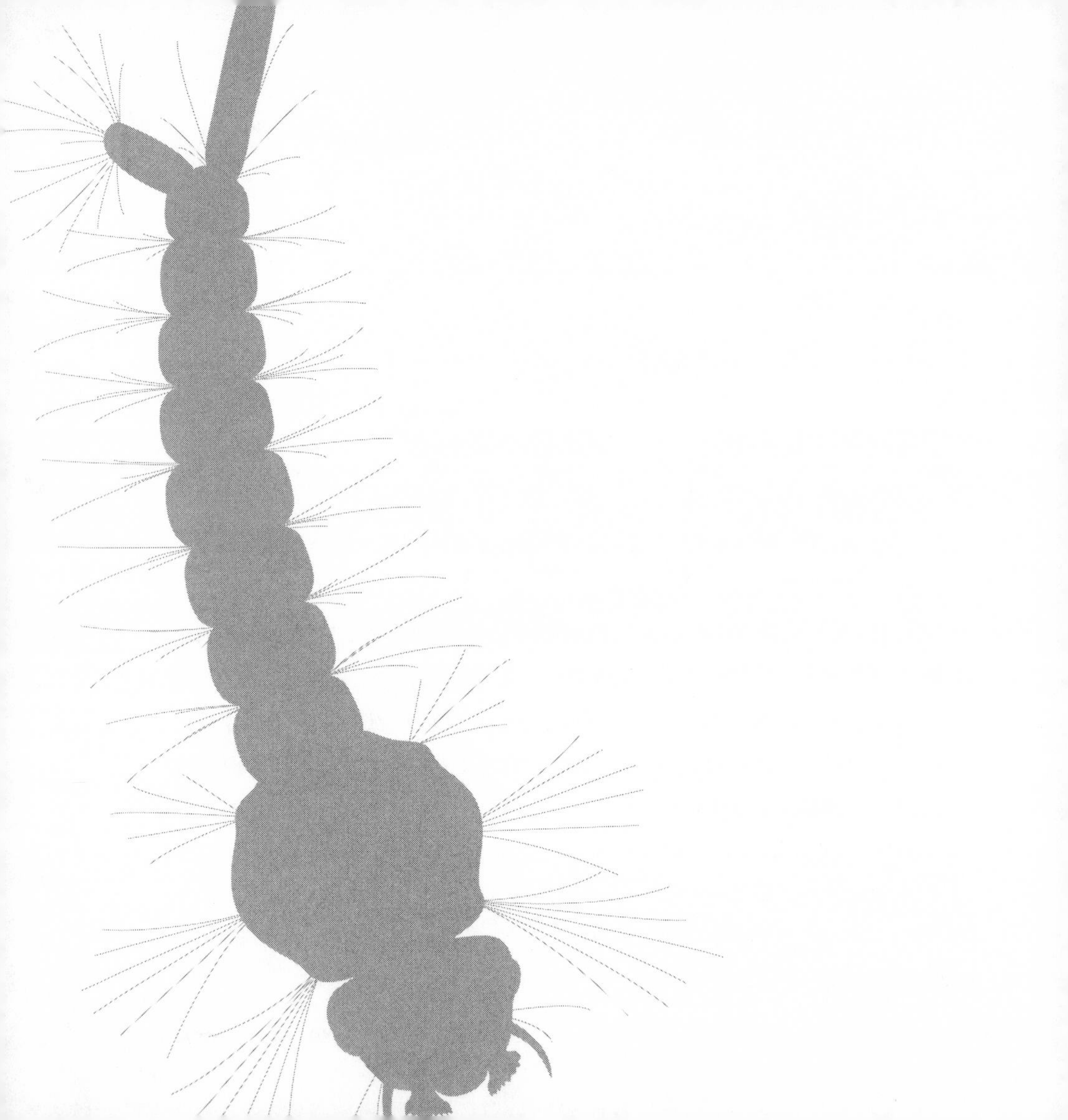

CHAPTER TWO

Not-Quite-Super Powers

The fates have decided that you've suffered enough repulsive ramifications. You've been up to your ears in boogers and up to your nose in earwax. You've been spit on, pooped on, and picked on. It's about time you deserved some good fortune. Yes, you are about to become extraordinary. You're getting a super power! Okay maybe they aren't all "super", but they're still pretty cool. Even better, you get to choose between two appetizing alternatives!

Would you rather...

be able to summon swarms of bugs

OR

be able to kill bugs with mini-lasers shot from your eyes?

Would you rather...

be able to scan documents into your computer with your tongue

OR

be able to weed-whack your lawn with your foot?

Would you rather...

have eyes that can change color to match your outfit

OR

tan in the pattern of desert camouflage?

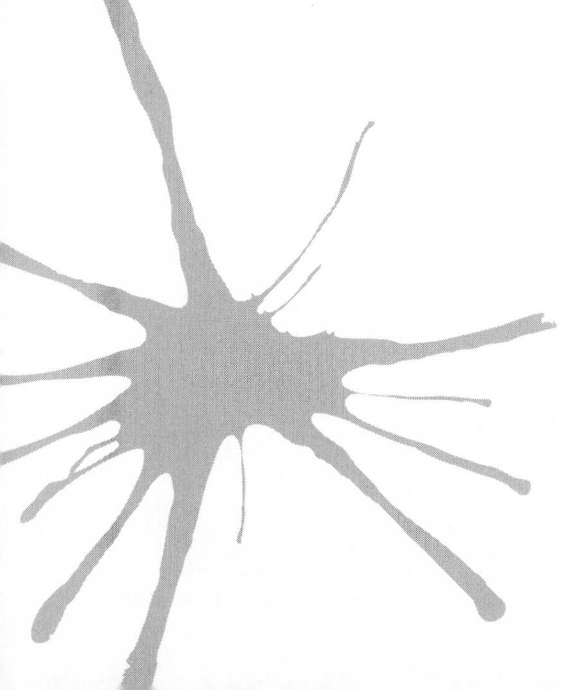

YOU MUST CHOOSE!

WOULD YOU RATHER....HAVE LEGO BOOGERS

OR FART CLASSICAL MUSIC?

Would you rather...

be able to stop and reload your life like in a video game

OR

have a cheat code that allows you to jump ahead and skip parts of your life?

What parts of your life would you rewind to?
What parts of your life would you skip?
What parts would you put in slow-motion if you could?

Would you rather...

have a "Get out of trouble at home" card (no matter what you do, one time, you won't get in trouble)

OR

have a "Get out of trouble at school" card (same rules)?

Would you rather...

have anything you touch turn to gold **OR** anything you touch turn to Silly Putty?

silver **OR** Nerf?

cheese **OR** become helium-filled?

Things to think about: touching furniture, pets, family, friends, enemies

Would you rather...

have the ability to temporarily swap parents with friends

OR

have the ability to temporarily swap facial features with friends?

Things to think about: parents who are good cooks, trading noses, having one eye that is a different color from the other, trading for freckles and making a cool design out of them

YOU MUST CHOOSE!

Would you rather...

poop fragrant flower petals

OR

be able to beam your pee from your bladder to the toilet?

Things to think about: never having to hold it, leaving bathrooms smelling great

YOU MUST CHOOSE!

WOULD YOU RATHER...HAVE FOLDABLE SWISS ARMY KNIFE DEVICES FOR FINGERNAILS

OR HAVE NUNCHUCKS FOR HAIR?

Which iPod app would you want...

one that takes a picture of someone and then tells you which celebrity they look the most like **OR** one that irons your clothes?

one that causes people to tell the truth **OR** one that beeps when someone who has a crush on you is near?

one that transforms into a boomerang **OR** one that shoots a blinding ray?

Would you rather...

have the ability to shrink down to one inch in height

OR

the ability to grow to 100 feet in height?

Would you rather...

have psychic visions of available parking spots

OR

have the ability to always choose the fastest checkout line?

YOU MUST CHOOSE!

Would you rather...

be able to talk to any animal

OR

be able to change into any animal?

Would you rather...

be a supervillain called the "Mime" who can mime objects into reality

OR

a supervillain called the "The Doorman"? (Weapons include keys and door knobs, and fighting style involves a lot of opening and closing doors.)

YOU MUST CHOOSE!

Would you rather...

have the ability to see the future, but only one second ahead

OR

have the ability to fly, but only in the inside of airplanes?

Would you rather...

have an hour-long chat with your 5-year-old self

OR

with your 40-year-old self?

If you could talk to your 5-year-old self, you can warn your younger self to avoid all the things that you didn't like. If you talk to your 40-year-old self, you can ask your older self about all the things you should do or avoid in the future! What would you ask? What would you say?

YOU MUST CHOOSE!

WOULD YOU RATHER...HAVE A SURPRISE FIST THAT POPS OUT OF YOUR CHEST ON A SPRING

OR HAVE CONFETTI THAT SHOOTS OUT OF YOUR ARMPITS DURING CELEBRATIONS?

Would you rather...

get straight "A"s without doing any work

OR

be the best in your school at sports without ever practicing?

Would you rather...

be able to make it snow on command

OR

be able to make people suddenly break-dance on command?

Things to think about: snow days, making your teacher suddenly dance while teaching; would you even want to miss school if you had the dancing power?

YOU MUST CHOOSE!

Would you rather...

be able to come in fourth in any race any time

OR

be able to perfectly forge anyone's handwriting but only when writing the phrase "I want pudding!"

Things to consider: selling forged President Obama signed photos (where he evidently wants everyone to know he wants pudding.)

You're trapped in medieval Europe.

Would you rather...

be the only person who knows modern medicine

OR

the only person who knows kung fu?

YOU MUST CHOOSE!

Would you rather...

have a fully working echolocation navigation system like bats have

OR

have fully functional kangaroo legs?

Things to consider: playing Marco Polo, slam-dunking in basketball

Would you rather...

have eyes that can make anyone you want fall in love with you

OR

have eyes that can turn your enemies to stone?

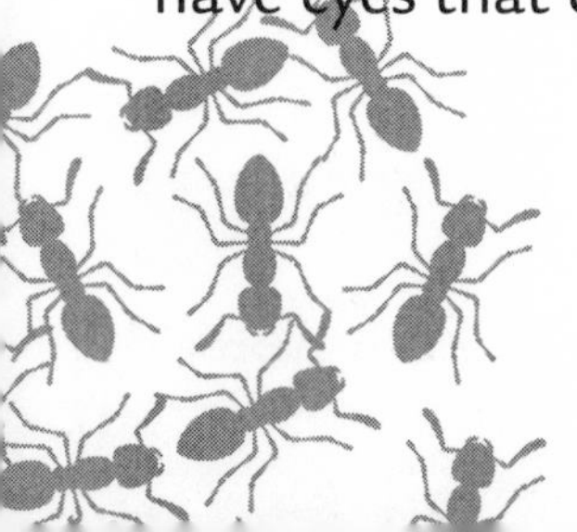

Would you rather...

have 7 samurai sworn to protect you **OR** 7 ninjas?

5 dragons **OR** 2 wizards?

400 hamsters **OR** 100 possessed staplers?

Would you rather...

have skin that lathers whenever you get wet

OR

have refrigerated pockets?

Things to consider: no need for soap, swimming, rainy days, keeping sandwiches in your pockets, reaching into your pockets on hot days

YOU MUST CHOOSE!

Would you rather...

be able to spit watermelon seeds with perfect accuracy up to fifty feet

OR

be able to fart to the tune of any song?

Would you rather...

have the ability to ace any test, but only when completely naked

OR

have the ability to be invisible but only while you dance around like an idiot?

YOU MUST CHOOSE!

Would you rather...

have a genetically-created caterpillar that crawls to wherever you have an itch and scratches it

OR

a genetically-created tiny hummingbird that cleans your nostrils, ears, belly button, and in between your toes?

Would you rather...

have your fingernails shaped into lock picks

OR

have a pony tail lasso?

Things to think about: never needing keys, life as a car thief, life as a sheriff

YOU MUST CHOOSE!

Would you rather...

be the most popular kid in school **OR** the fastest?

the smartest **OR** best-looking?

the best at staring contests **OR** the best at eating a head of lettuce the fastest?

Things to think about: With great power, comes great responsibility. With not much power, comes not much responsibility.

YOU MUST CHOOSE!

Would you rather...

have the ability to communicate with poodles **OR** pit bulls?

kittens **OR** elephants?

socks **OR** bagels?

Would you rather...

be unbeatable at Rock Paper Scissors

OR

unbeatable in kickball?

Would you rather...

have a voodoo mouse that allowed you to drag and drop people in real life as if they were on a computer screen

OR

have a photo-editing program that actually made people change to whatever you did to them on screen?

How would you use your drag and drop powers? Would you use them for good or evil? What photo-editing would you do? Who would you use it on? Would you give a female teacher sideburns? How about giving your gym teacher big red lipstick and eye shadow? Or making your brother cross-eyed with horns and plaid skin?

Would you rather...

have lemon-flavored hangnails

OR

have denim scabs?

Would you rather...

have the ability to teleport four feet to your left as often as you want

OR

the ability to teleport 100 miles once every month?

Things to think about: month-long vacations, fighting bullies, teleporting past thin walls (but make sure they are thin enough!)

YOU MUST CHOOSE!

Would you rather...

produce fudge in your belly button

OR

bubble gum in your ears?

Would you rather...

have the ability to make it snow cheese puffs

OR

be able to turn water into your favorite sugary drink?

If you had the power to bring back any three people from the grave, would you rather bring back...

Abe Lincoln, George Washington, and Martin Luther King, Jr.

OR

three of your relatives?

Who else would you bring back? What weird combinations of people in history can you think of?

Would you rather...

have ruby boogers

OR

have zits that grow into white pearls?

Would you rather...

get to change your name to whatever you want

OR

get to change your teachers' names to whatever you want?

Things to think about: Johnny Laser, Zargon the Great, Mr. Fartsville, Mrs. Tinkleballs

What name would you choose for yourself?

What name would you choose for your teachers? Might we suggest "Tinkleballs?"

YOU MUST CHOOSE!

WOULD YOU RATHER...COMMUTE TO SCHOOL ON A JETPACK
WOOSH!
SCHOOL

OR A RICKSHAW?
SCHOOL

Would you rather...

be able to expertly fight Kung Fu-style as long as you're singing "You're a Grand Old Flag"

OR

be able to answer all the teacher's questions correctly as long as you are madly playing air-guitar?

Would you rather...

be able to get revenge on the school bully by having a voodoo doll of him

OR

by having the ability to control all of his bodily functions?

Would you rather...

be given life-long "butting-in-line" privileges

OR

life-long "using bad word" privileges?

YOU MUST CHOOSE!

In order to defeat hostile enemies, would you rather make things into weapons from...

a supermarket **OR** a party store?

a baby supply store **OR** a shoe store?

a glass store **OR** a pet store?

WOULD YOU RATHER ...BE THE BEST RAPPER IN THE WORLD
WOULD YOU RAPPER M.C.

OR BE THE BEST WRAPPER IN THE WORLD?

3

CHAPTER THREE

Cruel and Unusual Punishments

Okay, so things have been going well for long enough. We're afraid it's back to the unbearable, unacceptable and unpleasant. It's time to again cringe and wince as you entertain the possibility of enduring one of the following unfortunate fates: fates that are perhaps a) painful, b) embarrassing, c) annoying, d) dangerous, or e) all of the above. ☺

Would you rather...

get caught picking your nose by someone you have a crush on

OR

rip a stinky, thunderous fart in the middle of an otherwise quiet school assembly?

Would you rather...

have to dance a ballet for two minutes in front of your entire school

OR

have to sing three pop songs in front of the entire school?

Would you rather...

lose your swim trunks halfway down a waterslide

OR

lose your lunch halfway down a roller coaster?

WOULD YOU RATHER...HAVE TO SPEND EVERY DINNER FOR A YEAR WITH YOUR PRINCIPAL

OR GET A TATTOO OF YOUR PRINCIPAL ON YOUR ARM?
PARLOR

Would you rather...

have to fight a half-sized version of your school's meanest bully

OR

a quadruple-sized version of your school's biggest geek?

Would you rather...

bite into a popsicle with your front teeth 20 times

OR

get a paper cut on your eye?

Would you rather...

have your thoughts automatically texted to your brother/sister's phone

OR

have your thoughts automatically texted to your mother's phone?

Would you rather...

be pegged nonstop for ten minutes with oranges **OR** eggs?

Koosh balls **OR** paper footballs?

nickels **OR** cantaloupes?

WOULD YOU RATHER...HAVE YOUR TWO TOP FRONT TEETH NEVER STOP GROWING

OR YOUR TWO FRONT BOTTOM TEETH NEVER STOP GROWING?

Would you rather...

have to talk like a robot for a whole day

OR

walk like a robot for a whole day?

Try doing each all day. See which annoys people first.

Would you rather...

wear (and use) diapers for a week

OR

travel everywhere by pink tricycle (complete with little cute tassels on the handlebars) for a week?

Would you rather...

live alone on a desert island for a month

OR

pick someone to live on the island with you for a year?

If you could pick anyone in the world to join you on an island, who would you pick? Who would you pick last? What objects would you pick if you could pick three? What music would you choose if you could pick three songs? What books? This one?

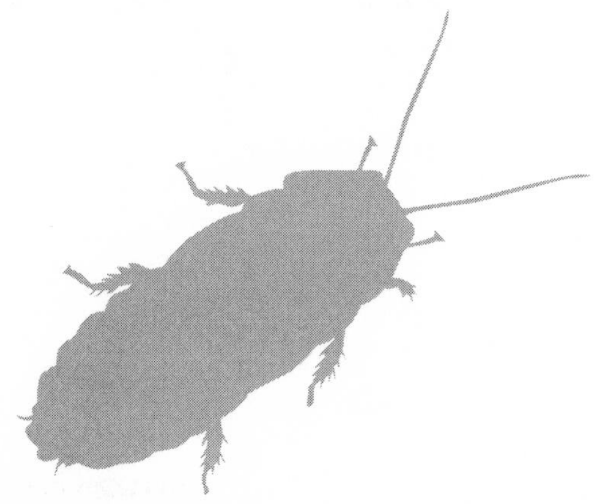

YOU MUST CHOOSE!

Would you rather...

shed your skin every week like a snake

OR

have to hibernate like a bear each winter from November to March?

Would you rather...

have your bedroom designed like a prison cell

OR

have an upside-down bedroom?

WOULD YOU RATHER...ONLY BE ABLE TO BATHE IN WASHING MACHINES

OR ONLY BE ABLE TO SLEEP CURLED UP IN A DRYER?

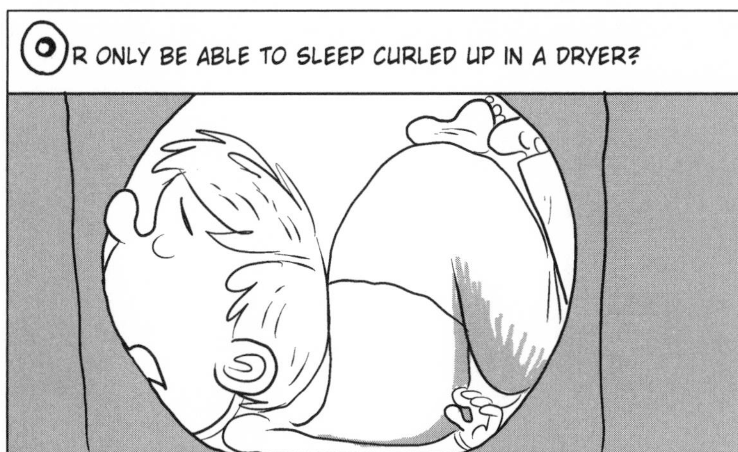

Would you rather...

get twisted up like a balloon animal

OR

be a human puck on a giant air hockey table?

Would you rather...

have a splinter stuck forever in your finger

OR

have it feel like your funny bone is hit all the time?

Would you rather...

have to wear a nose ring that is connected to an earring with only a two-inch chain

OR

have to wear a lip ring connected to a belly button ring with an eight-inch chain?

Would you rather...

be chased by a swarm of bees **OR** one really angry German Shepherd?

40 angry pigeons **OR** 3 angry weathermen?

10,000 crickets **OR** 1 angry Burger King mascot?

Would you rather...

only be able to whisper

OR

only be able to yell?

Things to consider: telling secrets, sounding mad when you're not, book reports

Would you rather...

kiss a poisonous jellyfish

OR

kiss (insert someone from school)?

Would you rather...

wear a rattlesnake as a belt

OR

wear an electric eel as a tie?

Would you rather...

your parents be required to always drive on the wrong side of the road

OR

be required to always drive in reverse?

Would you rather...

always get stuck behind someone at least a foot taller than you at every movie, concert, play, etc.

OR

always get stuck behind Slowface Johnson whenever you need to get somewhere fast on the street, at an airport, etc.?

Would you rather...

get body-slammed in the ring by World Wrestling Entertainment star John Cena

OR

get an atomic wedgie from Shaq?

Would you rather...

have to solve a Sudoku before you can open the refrigerator and any food cabinets

OR

have to solve a Sudoku before you can get into bed to go to sleep?

Would you get cranky when hungry? How would that affect your concentration? What about when you are exhausted and ready for bed? How about if you had to solve a puzzle before you could get out of bed? Would you become bed-ridden?

Would you rather...

get stuck on an elevator with gossipy girls **OR** businessmen talking loudly on their cell phones?

skunks **OR** angry sumo wrestlers?

100 hornets **OR** your 3 least favorite teachers?

Would you rather...

have a zero-gravity bedroom

OR

a zero-gravity classroom?

If ten thousand dollars depended on it, would you rather...

sink a free throw

OR

correctly answer five questions about geography?

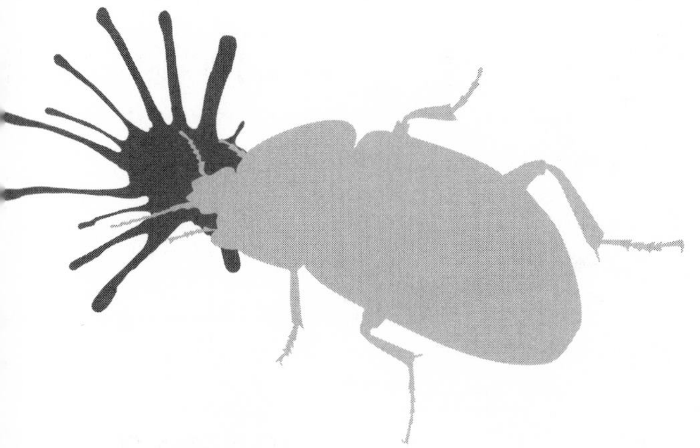

WOULD YOU RATHER...GET IN A SNOWBALL FIGHT AGAINST A MAJOR LEAGUE PITCHER

OR BE A TACKLING DUMMY FOR AN NFL LINEBACKER?

You just got in big trouble at school. Would you rather your punishment be...

to clean the school bathrooms with only a toothbrush

OR

to spend 24 hours straight listening to a podcast by (insert your most boring teacher)?

Would you rather...

have to wade through a dumpster full of garbage until you found a contact lens

OR

have to retrieve a penny as quickly as possible in a shallow pool full of piranha?

Would you rather...

your after-school job be mowing the lawn of a haunted mansion

OR

babysitting hyperactive quintuplets?

Would you rather...

have to wear three layers of sweats whenever you go to the beach

OR

have to wear your mom's bathing suit?

Would you rather...

survive by eating lima beans and mustard for a week

OR

brussell sprouts and prune juice?

Would you rather...

have one eyebrow singed off by a Bunsen burner

OR

have your left hand dyed purple?

If your life depended on it, would you rather...

gain one yard against a professional football team's defense

OR

score a single basket against LeBron James in a game of one-on-one basketball?

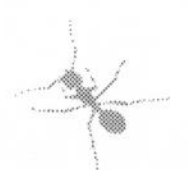

Would you rather...

have your face repeatedly paddled for five minutes by ping pong world champions

OR

have somebody do the "got your nose" trick and really rip off your nose?

Would you rather...

have a pebble sewn into the bottom of your left foot

OR

have a sesame seed lodged uncomfortably and permanently between your front teeth?

Would you rather...

have to eat 25 jalapeño peppers for breakfast each day

OR

drink a glass of blended insects?

Would you rather...

live with the certainty that at some point in your life you are going to be attacked by lions but not know when

OR

know exactly when it is going to happen?

Would you rather...

lose a day of summer vacation every time you misspell a word

OR

get grounded for a day any time you use a bad word?

Would you rather...

have a "Kick me!" sign taped to your back every day

OR

a "Dance with me!" sign?

Would you rather...

use a power drill as a Q-tip

OR

use sandpaper as toilet paper?

Would you rather...

have whatever you are thinking Tweeted (Twittered) to your parents every two minutes

OR

every two minutes, receive a Twitter tweet with whatever your parents are thinking?

Could you use your power to get out of trouble? Would you really want to know what your parents were thinking all the time?

YOU MUST CHOOSE!

Would you rather battle in the water...

3 manatees **OR** 300 flounder?

20,000 guppies **OR** 1 swordfish?

5 beavers **OR** Aquaman while he is busy doing his taxes?

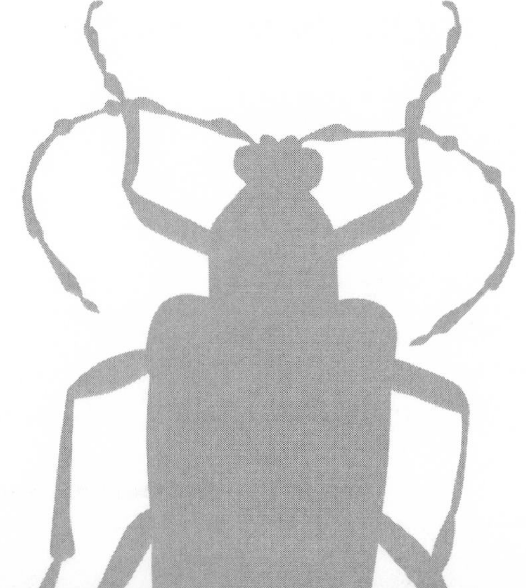

Would you rather...

be strapped to a table and have a drop of water repeatedly drip on your forehead

OR

be strapped to a table and have your eyes continuously pried open as you watch a one week marathon of *Dora the Explorer*?

YOU MUST CHOOSE!

Would you rather...

fight a creature with the body of a jaguar and the head of a cow

OR

fight a creature with the body of a horse and the head of Billy Ray Cyrus?

Would you rather...

have your thumbs smashed by a hammer

OR

have a five-inch screw slowly screwed into your navel?

WOULD YOU RATHER...BATTLE 10 PARAKEETS

OR FIVE POSSESSED WATERMELONS?

Would you rather...

once a week, have your dog actually eat your homework

OR

get sick for real any time you fake being sick to miss school?

Things to think about: letting your homework "pass through" your dog and then handing it in

Would you rather...

have to shower every day with poison ivy soap

OR

gargle every night with battery acid?

YOU MUST CHOOSE!

Would you rather...

for school punishment, have to re-alphabetize the entire collection of the school library

OR

have to cook the school cafeteria lunches for a full year?

Would you rather for $10,000...

have to ride a rhinoceros rodeo-style for at least eight seconds **OR** have to memorize word for word the front page of *The New York Times*?

have to beat Yoda in a staring contest **OR** have to eat 20 hot dogs in three minutes?

have to read all the entries for one letter out of the dictionary without mispronouncing anything **OR** have to count to 500,000 without messing up once?

YOU MUST CHOOSE!

Authors' Debate

Would you rather...

battle 100 Pillsbury Dough Boys

Bring It, Boys – David Gomberg

It'd be great fighting the Dough Boys. You'd feel like an all-powerful giant, flinging the bread-men off your body like flies, molding them to misshapen embarrassment; tearing their doughy flesh apart and devouring it like a monster. Some may say the Dough Boy cannot be killed, that it re-collects itself like a blob. But there are fool-proof ways of defeating Dough Boys: the toaster. One by one to the chamber of heat they will go, the assault of their doughy fists feeling like a gentle massage.

YOU MUST CHOOSE!

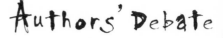

OR 20 Geese?

Geese, Please – Justin Heimberg

We know what geese are made of. Feathers and beak and flesh. What twisted anatomy dwells within the dark magic of the Dough Boy we cannot say. And you forget about the most deadly weapon of the Dough Boy: suffocation. They will stuff one another into your mouth, wrap tight around your nostrils and fuse into one massive doughboy. Remember there are 100 of them. You may volley and kick a dozen or so away at a time, but they will engulf you and you will soon find yourself in a doughy coffin.

YOU MUST CHOOSE!

CHAPTER FOUR

Weird, Wild, and Wacky

There's gross. There's cool. And then there's just plain weird. Weird doesn't have to be bad. Or good for that matter. It just needs to be... well, weird. Weird like having centipedes for eyelashes. Weird like sporting a beard of broccoli. Weird like your feet ending in little mouse heads instead of toes. Don't fear the weird! Instead, welcome the weirdness into your life and choose between two equally bizarre choices.

Would you rather...

have jellyfish tentacles for hair

OR

bat wings for ears?

Things to think about: stinging your own face, stinging your enemies, fanning yourself on hot days with your wings, getting haircuts

Would you rather...

have a solar-powered brain

OR

a battery-powered brain?

What would happen on rainy days? Who would replace your batteries? Would you replace them yourself when they are low and you start moving and speaking slowly?

YOU MUST CHOOSE!

Would you rather...

occasionally "lose reception" (like when on a cell phone) in conversation and be unable to hear what people are saying

OR

have a black hole belly button which sucks objects within two inches into nothingness?

Would you rather...

snore the sound of a chainsaw

OR

burp with the force of a bathroom hand dryer?

Would you rather...

have to wear a Snuggie in public every day

OR

have to wear an eye patch?

Things to think about: playing sports, school dances, sleeping on airplanes

Would you rather...

have to drink using only an eye dropper

OR

have to eat using only a thumbtack?

Would you rather...

have to keep a hard-boiled egg in your mouth at all times

OR

have an armadillo chained to your leg at all times?

Would you rather...

have 8 ears **OR** 36 nostrils?

10 eyes **OR** 24 fingers?

400 lips **OR** 8,000 toes?

YOU MUST CHOOSE!

WOULD YOU RATHER...AUTOMATICALLY HEAD BUTT ANYTHING YOU SEE THAT'S ORANGE
BUTT!

OR AUTOMATICALLY KISS ANYTHING THAT IS PURPLE?

Would you rather...

recite famous historical speeches in your sleep

OR

perform various swim strokes in your sleep?

Would you rather...

say the word "porridge" every other word as in: "Hi porridge, how porridge have porridge you porridge been?"

OR

have a strange condition where anytime you walk into a room, dozens of pickles fall on your head?

Would you rather...

do a spit take on the first sip anytime you drink something

OR

shout "Follow that car, and step on it!" every time you get into a vehicle?

Things to think about: riding the school bus, fancy dinners, school lunches

Would you rather...

respond to danger (and awkward situations) by playing dead like a possum

OR

by squirting ink like a squid?

What happens when a crush approaches you?
What are you afraid of?
What is awkward for you?

YOU MUST CHOOSE!

Would you rather...

have to walk with your feet never leaving the ground

OR

never be able to use the same word twice in any given 24-hour period?

Things to think about: Try both for a day.

Would you rather...

cry Tabasco sauce

OR

vibrate intensely instead of laughing?

Would you rather...

be able shoot mustard from your eyes

OR

be able to extend one eyeball up, out and around corners like a submarine periscope?

Would you rather...

have to make your living as a subway pick-pocket

OR

a subway yodeling street performer?

Would you rather...

only be able to enter rooms by Kool-Aid Man-style wall crashes

OR

only be able to exit rooms by jumping through a window as if fleeing a burning building?

Would you rather...

have baby-sized feet

OR

baby-sized hands?

Things to think about: sports, writing, toppling, finding shoes

Would you rather always have to wear...

a catcher's mitt **OR** snowshoes?

Lady Gaga's outfits **OR** a suit of armor?

clothes made of fresh fish **OR** clothes made of spider webs?

WOULD YOU RATHER...YOUR PARENTS HAVE TO DRIVE TWICE THE SPEED LIMIT
ZOOM!

OR HALF THE SPEED LIMIT?

WOULD YOU RATHER...HAVE REGENERATING GUMMY WORM HAIR
POONT!
Chew
Chew

OR DIME BOOGERS?
DENTIST
CANDY & ICE CREAM
STORE
10

Would you rather...

not be able to tell the difference between sandwiches and Frisbees

OR

between chalk and lip balm?

Would you rather...

only be able to fall asleep on subway cars

OR

always wake up on top of a random building?

Would you rather be able to move with your mind:

bowling pins **OR** motorcycles?

cauliflower **OR** worms?

silverware **OR** markers?

Things to think about: How would you use your powers?

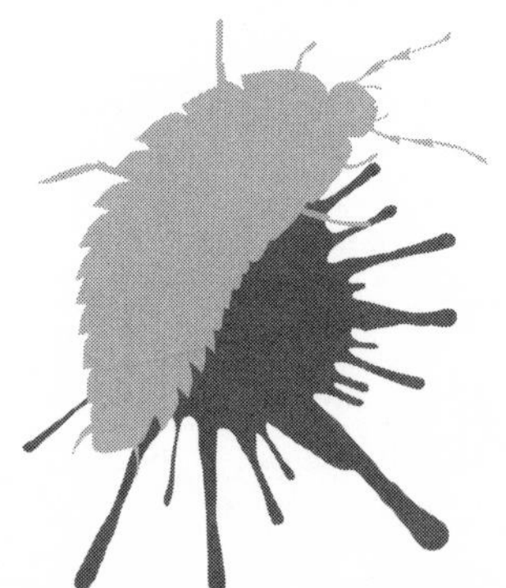

Would you rather...

have a rare speech problem where your moving lips and voice don't match like in an old Kung Fu movie

OR

get attacked once a day like in a Kung Fu movie (you always win the battle, but you feel the pain of the fight)?

Would you rather...

have Vulcan ears

OR

a Vulcan personality?

Would you rather...

speak as if you are always out of breath

OR

speak as if you are using an auto tuner (the thing that makes singers sound robotic)?

Would you rather...

be fluent in Latin

OR

Pig-Latin?

Would you rather...

always be looking the wrong way in photographs

OR

always have a little bit of spinach stuck in your teeth?

Would you rather...

speak like a wise Native American chief whenever you're chilly

OR

sprout facial hair at the first sign of traffic, with it getting worse as road congestion does?

Would you rather...

sneeze a blast of shotgun pellets

OR

have an iguana head for a tongue?

Things to think about: the angle of your head when sneezing; the kick-back of a sneeze, kissing

Would you rather...

not be able to tell the difference between keys and Q-tips

OR

between chairs and puppies?

Things to think about: painful ear-swabbing, frustration trying to get inside your home, getting odd looks as you stroke and talk silly to a chair, sitting on a poor pup

YOU MUST CHOOSE!

Would you rather...

have poppy-seeded skin

OR

have asparagus for hair?

Would you rather...

be covered in an oozing green slime all the time

OR

instead of tanning when in the sun, turn polka-dotted?

YOU MUST CHOOSE!

WOULD YOU RATHER...HAVE A HELIUM-FILLED BODY

OR A LEAD-FILLED BODY?
FINISH

Would you rather...

have to battle a blindfolded Bengal tiger **OR** 600 yipping poodles?

your own left hand **OR** your own right foot?

Medusa when her shoes keep coming untied **OR** a Minotaur who is looking for his keys during the battle?

Would you rather...

wear crumb-filled potato chip bags for socks

OR

oven mitts for shoes?

Things to think about: itchiness, rocky surfaces, heating up your mitts on cold days

Would you rather legally change your name to...

"Remulon" **OR** "Gorgorath?"

"The (insert your name here)" **OR** "(insert your name here) of the Mountain People"?

the sound of a glass shattering **OR** the smell of vanilla?

With the last question, how would people call out your name? How would you communicate your name? Which would be trickier?

YOU MUST CHOOSE!

Would you rather always be age...

5 **OR** 35?

12 **OR** 50?

2 **OR** 62?

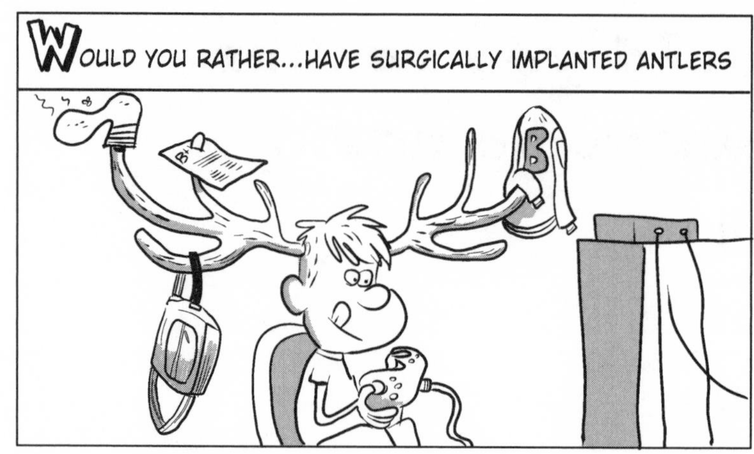
WOULD YOU RATHER...HAVE SURGICALLY IMPLANTED ANTLERS

OR A SURGICALLY IMPLANTED ELEPHANT TRUNK?

Would you rather...

look like this

OR

look like this?

Would you rather...

have ears that face backwards

OR

eyes that blink sideways?

Would you rather...

anytime you meet someone, give them a friendly noogie

OR

anytime you're in a restaurant, always try to whip the tablecloths off the tables without upsetting the dishes (but seldom succeed)?

Things to think about: meeting new teachers, meeting nuns, family reunion dinners

YOU MUST CHOOSE!

Would you rather...

be reincarnated as a piece of belly-button lint

OR

as a doorknob?

Would you rather...

have no arms and legs and have to slither around like a snake

OR

have short stubby arms and legs and a heavy turtle-like shell on your back which you can retract into?

Would you rather...

have an extra eye on the back of your head

OR

have an extra arm on your back?

Would you rather...

have tennis ball-sized eyeballs

OR

coffee mug-sized nostrils?

Would you rather...

grow three inches any time someone says "Hello" but shrink five inches any time someone says "Goodbye"

OR

grow six inches any time someone says "Hello" and shrink one inch anytime someone says "Goodbye?"

Think about an average day. How many inches would you grow or shrink based on the numbers above? Can you think of any ways to control your growth/ shrinkage?

YOU MUST CHOOSE!

Would you rather...

be unable to stop from tackling anyone over 75 years old

OR

grow a bushy beard every day on a different part of your body?

Things to think about: visiting a retirement home, knee-beards, foot beards, forehead beards

Would you rather...

have extra eyeballs in the palms of your hands

OR

ears that you can detach and use to transmit sound directly to your head?

Would you rather...

have a ring of hair around each eye

OR

have earlobes that connected under your chin?

Would you rather...

have gingerbread-scented farts

OR

sweat butter?

WOULD YOU RATHER...BE CONSTANTLY COMPELLED TO CHASE SQUIRRELS AND MAILMEN LIKE DOGS
MAIL
WOOF WOOF

OR CASUALLY CRAWL ONTO PEOPLE'S LAPS TO TAKE NAPS LIKE A CAT?
Purrrrh

Would you rather...

for the rest of your life, instead of walking, have to do cartwheels

OR

have to skip?

Would you rather...

always put things off until later

OR

(work in progress)?

Authors' Debate

Would you rather...

have all your eye-blinks last 10 seconds

Anti-yawn – Justin Heimberg

Follow me, here. You yawn when you are tired. You cannot fall asleep when you are yawning. Therefore, you will never get any sleep. Your two-hour yawns will keep you up. You will then become more and more tired each hour, each day, increasingly yawning, and becoming less able to sleep. Eventually you will go crazy and wander the streets known as the Yawner, a creature of myth that people both desire and fear to see. Your mouth will open and close on its own, making chewing impossible, until your diet will be all smoothie and the bugs that will fly into your open yawning mouth.

YOU MUST CHOOSE!

OR have all your yawns last two hours?

Anti-blink – David Gomberg

We blink often—an average of 20 times per minute, according to the second thing that came up when I Googled it. That means there are only a few seconds between blinks. Do the math. This means your eyes will be closed at about a 3:1 ratio. 10 seconds closed, 3 seconds open. You are half-blind, not in one eye, and not with bad vision, but half the time. Reading would be too tough to deal with. Riding a bike? Forget about it. You'd always be the one screwing up family pictures. You'd be a constant blinking disappointment.

YOU MUST CHOOSE!

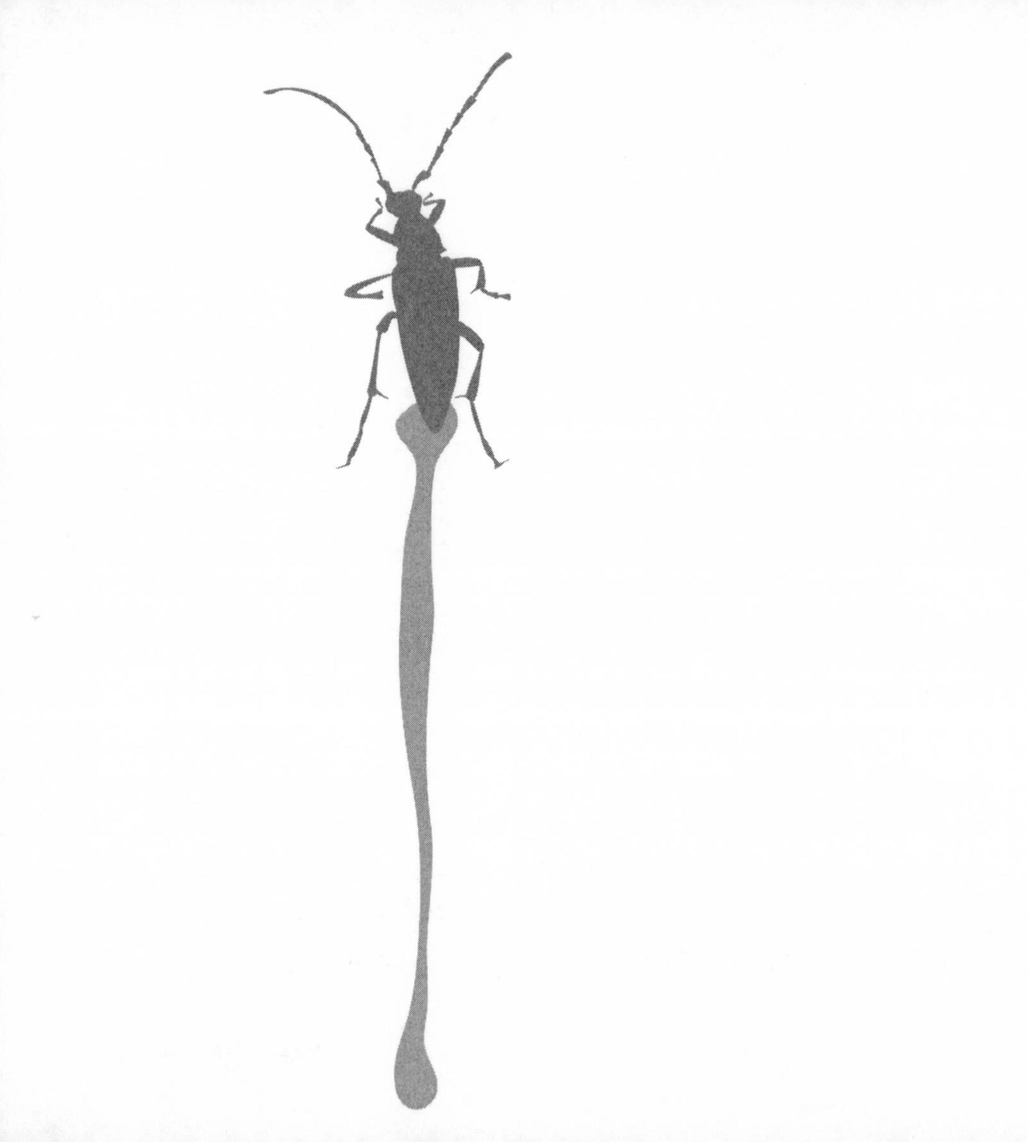

CHAPTER FIVE

Really Repulsive

What's grosser than gross? Answer: Repulsive. So then, what's more repulsive than repulsive? Answer: Really Repulsive. Yep, this time the boogers are bigger, the trash is trashier, and the guts are gutsier. The hills of dog doo have swelled to mountains, and the trickling streams of snot are now raging rivers. It'd be almost poetic if it weren't so sickening. (Oh, and don't bother closing your eyes. It won't help. It'll just make the smells seem stronger!)

Would you rather...

sleep in a bed of rotting fruit every night

OR

in a pile of dead spiders?

Would you rather...

find an eyeball in the middle of the Blow Pop that you were licking

OR

find a dead frog at the bottom of the Coke you just drank?

YOU MUST CHOOSE!

Would you rather...

use a dead flounder as soap

OR

use garlic cloves as deodorant?

Would you rather have a bird poop...

in your hair **OR** on your brand new bike?

in your ear **OR** all over your clothes?

on your cheek **OR** on your sandwich?

YOU MUST CHOOSE!

Would you rather...

eat a jumbo cotton candy made of spider webs

OR

suck on a boxful of animal eye gobstoppers (no biting)?

Would you rather eat ice cream that is flavored...

meatloaf (with beef chunks) **OR** brussel sprouts (with whole sprouts)?

pencil lead **OR** super spicy jalapeño pepper ice cream?

garlic **OR** vanilla ant farm special?

WOULD YOU RATHER...CARPOOL TO SCHOOL WITH A ZOMBIE
UNGH!
BRAINS!

OR A WEREWOLF?

Would you rather...

suffer from ingrown eyelashes

OR

eyeball warts?

YOU MUST CHOOSE!

Which Doomsday Scenario would you rather see happen?

The Earth is struck by a meteor shower of giant wet, nasty boogers sneezed from aliens as big as moons, bombarding the planet with boogers the size of houses and causing tidal waves of thick gooey snot

OR

The Earth is struck by a giant poop asteroid, covering the planet in poop, blotting out the sun with poop and raining poop from the skies, plunging the Earth into a nuclear poop winter?

WOULD YOU RATHER...EAT PASTA BOILED IN A PUBLIC BATHROOM'S TOILET WATER

OR EAT PORK CHOPS TOPPED WITH A SAUCE MADE OF TOBACCO SPIT COLLECTED FROM PRO BASEBALL PLAYERS?

Would you rather...

lick clean the inside of a horse's nostril

OR

have a horse lick the insides of your nostril?

Would you rather...

uncontrollably fart while reciting the Pledge of Allegiance

OR

uncontrollably belch when singing the "Star Spangled Banner"?

Would you rather...

shed your teeth every week like a tiger shark

OR

leave a trail of slime like a snail?

Would you rather...

lick clean every Skeeball from a Chuck E. Cheese

OR

have to milk a cow with your mouth until a bucket is full?

Would you rather...

consume a sundae of pig stomach drizzled with hot pus, sprinkled with mice droppings, topped with the eye of a gnu

OR

eat a six inch tall spiky cactus?

Would you rather...

drink a tall glass of melted cheese

OR

drop a Mentos in a glass of Diet Coke and immediately take a swig?

Note: Do not try this or anything else in this book at home!

YOU MUST CHOOSE!

Would you rather...

have to wear clothes taken daily from (insert someone gross)'s dirty hamper

OR

sleep each night in a bed recently occupied by (insert another gross person)?

Would you rather...

bathe in a tub of maggots

OR

bathe in the thick gooey fat drained from Hollywood actress's liposuction treatments?

Would you rather...

get sprayed by a skunk in the eyes

OR

in the mouth?

Would you rather...

have a lawnmower run over a cow patty and splatter you with its smelly chopped-up bits

OR

have to clean out a soiled hamster's cage with your bare hands?

YOU MUST CHOOSE!

Would you rather...

be climbing up a ladder and feel something splatter

OR

be sliding into first and feel something burst?

Would you rather...

breathe through your navel

OR

your butt?

Things to think about: snorkeling, wearing baggy pants to give you some breathing room, if you have an outie or innie

YOU MUST CHOOSE!

WOULD YOU RATHER...HAVE AN ACTUAL BEEHIVE HAIRDO

Would you rather...

have to share a gym locker with the world's sweatiest man

OR

share a camping tent with the world's gassiest man?

Things to think about: waking up in a puddle; Does your tent have good ventilation?

Would you rather...

eat some jumbo fried shrimp only to find out they were zombie fingers

OR

have a zombie eat your pinkie toe?

WOULD YOU RATHER...BE ABLE TO TOAST BREAD WITH YOUR ARMPITS
PEANUT BUTTER
BREAD

OR HAVE ALL YOUR BLACKHEAD PIMPLES PRODUCE HOT FUDGE WHEN SQUEEZED?
SPLAT!

WOULD YOU RATHER... BECOME INTERNATIONALLY FAMOUS FOR YOUR BOOGER ART
$8,000
BANK

OR BECOME A RESPECTED MUSICIAN BASED ON YOUR ARMPIT FARTING?
FA-FA-FA-
FART!

Would you rather...

be eating a burrito and discover a long, long hair in your mouth

OR

be licking a Tootsie Pop, only to find a fossil of an ancient insect in the middle?

Would you rather...

eat four scoops of hair from a barber shop floor and then cough up a cigar-shaped hairball like a cat

OR

eat a regurgitated cat hairball?

Would you rather...

roll around in a pit of worms

OR

let hundreds of beetles crawl all over you?

Would you rather...

wear a hat full of sour cream all day

OR

underwear full of crickets?

Would you rather...

for five minutes, sit in a hot tub full of bubbling camel spit

OR

lie in a closed coffin full of rat droppings?

Would you rather...

have a slingshot with unlimited booger ammo

OR

have a special blow-dart gun that blows pockets of fart-stench?

Would you rather...

dive through a Slip-N-Slide covered in thumbtacks **OR** maggots?

gasoline **OR** New England clam chowder?

blister juice **OR** sheep excrement?

Would you rather...

drink a trout smoothie

OR

eat a tarantula wrap?

Things to think about: What if the tarantula was still alive?

Would you rather...

have grape-flavored blood

OR

barbecue sauce saliva?

Things to think about: eating ribs, nosebleeds

Would you rather...

after sneezing, use a piece of used tissue **OR** just use your shirt?

use the American flag hanging in your classroom **OR** an unsuspecting friend's jacket sleeve?

use your pet **OR** your brother?

Would you rather...

be able to pick any time for your bedtime

OR

be able to pick any nose anytime (including your own)?

Would you rather...

still eat baby food

OR

still wear diapers?

Would you rather...

have an air freshener in your house that sends out the smell of thick pungent B.O.

OR

have a carpet of permanently wet dog hair?

Would you rather...

have shoelaces made of bloodworms

OR

wear a live lobster as a tie?

Would you rather...

have to walk around for a full day with your finger in your ear

OR

walk around all day carrying a 20-pound bowling ball?

Would you rather...

use your mouth to change a light bulb

OR

to flush a public toilet?

WOULD YOU RATHER...NEVER AGAIN CUT YOUR FINGER NAILS

OR YOUR HAIR?

Would you rather...

have a teacher who yells at you when you get something wrong

OR

a teacher whose spit flies seven feet when he talks?

Would you rather...

sleep nightly in pajamas made of dentists' used gauze

OR

have to reach into a walrus's mouth every time you want the key to your home?

YOU MUST CHOOSE!

Authors' Debate

Would you rather...

have Parmesan cheese dandruff

Cheese Please – David Gomberg

Bubble wrap acne has no function. It is a useless deformity. Parmesan cheese dandruff, on the other hand, is wonderfully useful. Parmesan goes well on anything, and a little goes a long way. So if you're out in a restaurant and you get some spaghetti, all it takes is a shake of the head, and you're good. Who wants to be addicted to popping their own face? People go through years of therapy for that. Pizza, pasta, vegetables, they all come alive with a little of the magic from your head and shoulders.

OR bubble wrap pimples?

That's a wrap – Justin Heimberg

There are few joys as wildly enjoyable as popping bubble wrap. It's irresistibly satisfying. Anytime you're bored, just can pop a bubble zit and get that crackle of satisfaction. Either one at a time, or if you have a rather bad breakout, a bunch at once. So, your face will look like a cross between a pepperoni pizza and phone packaging. Big deal. Your bubble-pocked face will be smiling ear to ear in joy.

6

CHAPTER SIX

Fantasies and Blessings

Today is going to be a good day. Life is not handing you any more lemons, so rotten and moldy, that the lemonade you make from them is undrinkable. Life isn't throwing you any more unhittable curveballs either. Nope, Life is setting up wonderful possibilties for you on a tee. You can't miss. All you need to do is swing away and pick one of two fantastic and blessed options.

Would you rather...

your school cafeteria have a soda machine that can mix flavors

OR

a candy lab that can mix candies and flavors together? What flavor sodas would you make? What flavors and candies would you make? What would you call your creations?

YOU MUST CHOOSE!

Would you rather...

grow up to be a rock star **OR** an astronaut?

an architect **OR** a zookeeper?

a matador **OR** a professional new-snack tester?

a belly-button lint sculptor **OR** a window-washer who performs song and dance routines as if in a musical while you work?

YOU MUST CHOOSE!

WOULD YOU RATHER... HAVE YOUR FACE CARVED INTO MT. RUSHMORE

OR HAVE YOUR BUTT CARVED INTO MT. RUSHMORE?

Would you rather...

be allowed to destroy Lego Land, pretending you are a giant monster

OR

be allowed to have a paintball war in your school? What would be your strategy in paintball? What would you hide behind? Who would you go after first? What kind of monster would you pretend to be in Lego Land? How would you go about destroying things?

Would you rather...

play video games for a job when you get older but make only minimum wage

OR

be a dog-pooper-scooper and make $100,000 a year?

Would you rather...

live on the International Space Station for a month

OR

on a tropical island?

Would you rather...

have Thomas Edison help you with all your science homework

OR

have George Washington Carver as your personal chef?

Things to think about: winning the science fair, peanut pie, peanut butter-covered peanuts, peanut smoothies, peanut forks

YOU MUST CHOOSE!

Would you rather...

have a star on the Hollywood Walk of Fame

OR

have a deli sandwich named after you?

Would you rather...

that your house was designed by Dr. Seuss

OR

MC Escher?

Things to think about: Google MC Escher to see his designs.

YOU MUST CHOOSE!

Would you rather...

your dreams were written by Roald Dahl (author of *Charlie and the Chocolate Factory*) **OR** Maurice Sendak (author of *Where the Wild Things Are*)?

Jeff Kinney (author of *Diary of a Wimpy Kid*) **OR** James Cameron (writer of *Avatar*)?

Lewis Carroll (author of *Alice and Wonderland*) **OR** by yourself?

YOU MUST CHOOSE!

Would you rather...

have a piece of magic gum that can taste like anything you think of

OR

a piece of gum with which you can blow a ten-foot bubble?

Things to think about: being lifted into the air, popping, chicken-pot-pie gum followed by hot fudge sundae

Would you rather...

have a built-in stereo system on your bike

OR

a soft-serve ice cream machine?

YOU MUST CHOOSE!

Would you rather never get...

tired **OR** hungry?

angry **OR** sad?

B.O. **OR** gas?

guilty **OR** embarrassed?

called "Dorkazon 2000" **OR** hit in the head with a pineapple?

Would you rather interview...

Barack Obama **OR** Carmelo Anthony?

Justin Bieber **OR** Angelina Jolie?

the ghost of Thomas Jefferson **OR** the ghost of Einstein?

Would you rather...

have Yoda **OR** Dumbledore as your personal bodyguard?

have Boba Fett as your personal housekeeper **OR** Yoda as your school guidance counselor?

look like Yoda and be as wise as he is **OR** not?

Would you rather...

change the National Anthem to "Pants on the Ground" (made famous on *American Idol*)

OR

change the words to the Pledge of Allegiance to the "Diarrhea Song?"

Things to consider: Place your hand over your heart and try both.

Would you rather your English papers be written by...

Shakespeare **OR** Snoop Dogg?

Martin Luther King, Jr. **OR** Benjamin Franklin?

your mom **OR** your dad?

Would you rather...

have a kangaroo butler

OR

a monkey chauffeur?

Would you rather...

have access to live webcams of every room in the White House

OR

every room in your neighbors' houses?

Would you rather...

watch your parents have a freestyle rap battle

OR

watch your parents have a freestyle dance battle?
Have your parents try it.
How about your teachers?

YOU MUST CHOOSE!

WOULD YOU RATHER...LIVE IN A WORLD WHERE FOOD CAN BE DOWNLOADED
DOWNLOADING

OR WHERE YOUR DREAMS CAN?

Would you rather...

sled down a hill of frozen ice cream

OR

slide down a fruit punch slide at a water park?

Would you rather...

have your favorite soda in the school water fountains

OR

have go-cart tracks on your school's playground?

Would you rather...

have LeBron James as your gym teacher

OR

Carrie Underwood as your music teacher?

Would you rather...

get to play on your favorite professional sports team for the championship game

OR

get to deliver the President's State of the Union address?

Would you rather...

get ahead in life using your mind

OR

your looks?

Would you rather...

hit a $50 million lottery

OR

own your own island?

Would you rather...

win a Grammy **OR** an Oscar?

an Emmy **OR** a Tony?

a pro sport's MVP prize **OR** the Nobel Peace Prize?

Would you rather...

have your parents go on *Dancing with the Stars* **OR** *America's Got Talent*?

The Biggest Loser **OR** *What Not to Wear?*

The Apprentice **OR** *Top Chef?*

YOU MUST CHOOSE!

WOULD YOU RATHER...BE TERRIFIED OF TRIANGLES

OR OF THE NUMBER 4?
4:44

Would you rather...

discover another planet

OR

a new species?

Would you rather...

have an element on the periodic chart named after you

OR

invent a type of new dance craze that sweeps the country? What would your element be called? What would your dance be? What else would you want named after you?

WOULD YOU RATHER...THAT ALL THE STAIRS IN YOUR HOUSE WERE REPLACED WITH CHUTES AND LADDERS

OR ALL THE FLOORS WERE MADE OF MOONBOUNCE MATERIAL?
BOUNCE!

Would you rather...

never miss a basketball shot

OR

always hit a home run?

Would you rather...

get to be a guest judge on *American Idol*

OR

get to force one of your friends to go on it?

Would you rather...

have a bedroom designed by the people that make James Bond contraptions

OR

have a bike designed by them?

Would you rather...

be able to make any food taste like any other food

OR

be able to teleport food from one plate to another? What would you teleport onto your plate? What would you teleport off of your plate? Where would you send it to?

Would you rather...

have every toy ever made

OR

$1 million?

Would you rather...

without any consequences, shove a pie in the class bully's face

OR

throw eggs at the principal?

Would you rather...

get around by hovercraft

OR

pet dragon?

Would you rather...

live in a planetarium

OR

an amusement park?

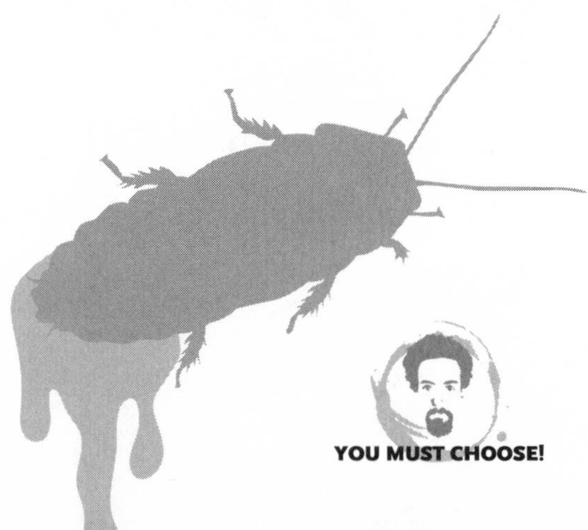

Would you rather...

get to star in your own TV show

OR

get to star on any professional sports team?

Would you rather...

be a character in *Avatar*

OR

a character in *Harry Potter*?

Would you rather...

find buried treasure

OR

ride on a UFO?

Would you rather...

ride shotgun in a NASCAR race

OR

be the holder for an extra point kicked in an NFL game? Which seems scarier?

Would you rather...

build a skatepark in your backyard

OR

a water park?

Would you rather...

have a retractable ballpoint pen in your finger

OR

have a laser pointer finger?

CHAPTER SEVEN

Really, Really Repulsive

Our sources tell us you have yet to be entirely grossed out. (Don't ask how we know. We have our ways.) Somehow you've managed to endure the repulsive and even withstand the really repulsive. You leave us no choice. We're rolling out the big guns. Here then are the revoltingly repugnant, radically rotten, ridiculously ridunculous, really, really repulsive.

Would you rather...

have a breakfast of booger-filled sausage links

OR

bacon strips made from cow tongues left out in the sun?

Would you rather...

eat a horse eye and cricket shish kabob marinated in camel spit

OR

a salad of giant cockroaches and moth wings tossed in dog slobber dressing?

YOU MUST CHOOSE!

Would you rather...

have to stuff your underwear with peanut butter

OR

birdseed?

Things to think about: birds, crusting

Would you rather...

fart out of your ears

OR

cry out of your nostrils?

YOU MUST CHOOSE!

WOULD YOU RATHER...HAVE HAIR MADE OF SLUGS

OR SPIDERS HANGING FROM WEB STRANDS?

Would you rather...

have to eat Spaghetti with Super balls

OR

Macaroni and Horse Snot?

Would you... eat a scab-topped pizza to avoid eating vegetables for a month?

It's time to do your daily chores.

Every day, would you rather...

have to unclog any clogged toilets in your neighborhood

OR

have to hand wash all of (insert gross teacher)'s underwear?

YOU MUST CHOOSE!

Would you rather...

play basketball against a gross, flabby, hairy shirtless sweaty old dude

OR

play tackle football against a 300 pounder?

Would you rather...

spend a night sleeping in an unclean elephant zoo cage

OR

stomach 50 cow farts in a row, standing two-inches behind the cow?

YOU MUST CHOOSE!

Would you rather...

shove a straw into a big blister and suck away

OR

use a Q-tip of poison ivy?

Would you rather...

have potato bug dandruff that combs your hair

OR

head lice that braids your hair?

Would you rather...

get caught in a mucus avalanche

OR

get rolled up in a giant dung ball by a giant 10-foot-tall dung beetle?

Would you rather...

eat a Twinkie filled with caterpillar guts

OR

eat a Nutty Buddy rolled in used kitty litter?

Would you rather...

eat some crispy cereal only to find out it wasn't cereal at all but just two-year-old milk with moldy, thick chunks in it

OR

eat a bowl of linguini only to find out it was a bowl of flatworms?

YOU MUST CHOOSE!

Would you rather...

get licked on the face by a giraffe

OR

stand behind a hippo as it leaves the water?

Did you know giraffes use their 18-inch tongues to clean out their own nostrils? Did you know hippos are known to use their tails to fling feces at others as they leave the water? Now what's your choice?

WOULD YOU RATHER...HAVE A MAGIC PENCIL THAT ALWAYS WROTE THE RIGHT ANSWERS
3.14 = B + C + Z +
A + BOAT = CHEESE
Z - F - YAHOO +
OWL + 3 X 9 1
APPLE
GENIUS!

OR HAVE THE ABILITY TO MAKE OTHER PEOPLE'S PENCILS WRITE WHATEVER YOUR WANT?
Q: Who was the first President?
A: President Doo-Doo McFARTSVILLE

Would you rather...

have a tadpole crawl up your nose and stay there as it turned into a frog

OR

have a spider lay an egg sac in your ear until the eggs hatched?

Would you rather...

dissect a frog with your bare hands

OR

catch a fish with your bare hands?

WOULD YOU RATHER... HAVE SUCH BAD DANDRUFF THAT IT LOOKS LIKE 2 INCHES OF SNOW HAVE FALLEN WHEREVER YOU ARE

Would you rather...

eat live cockroaches **OR** dead rats?

rotten meat **OR** spoiled milk?

a cocoon with a caterpillar in it **OR** a cocoon with a butterfly in it?

everything you find at the bottom of a school desk **OR** everything you find in between your sofa cushions?

a rotten-egg-and-moldy-cheese sandwich **OR** an ice cream-and-pus milkshake?

For $100, would you eat...

a spoonful of ear wax?

a bowl of tree bark?

a pile of dog hair?

a cupcake that landed face down on a dirty carpet (you picked it up after 3 seconds on the ground)?

a cupcake that landed face down on a dirty carpet (you picked it up after 30 seconds on the ground)?

WOULD YOU RATHER...BE SUPER-INTELLIGENT BUT ONLY WHILE PICKING YOUR NOSE
IF YOU TAKE THE SQUARE ROOT OF THE HYPOTENUSE OF THE TRIANGLE AND DIVIDE BY PI...
4
+3
7
3.14

OR BE INCREDIBLY FAST BUT ONLY WHILE CROSSING YOUR EYES?
SPIN!
SPIN!
FINISH LINE!
4
7

WOULD YOU RATHER... LIVE IN A WORLD WHERE CITIES ARE INFESTED WITH FLOATING AIR SHARKS
P-YOW!

OR WHERE THEY ARE FULL OF GIANT STREET SQUIDS?

Would you rather...

have armpit hair that grows an inch a minute

OR

toenails that grow an inch a minute?

Things to consider: shoes, wearing short sleeves, swimming

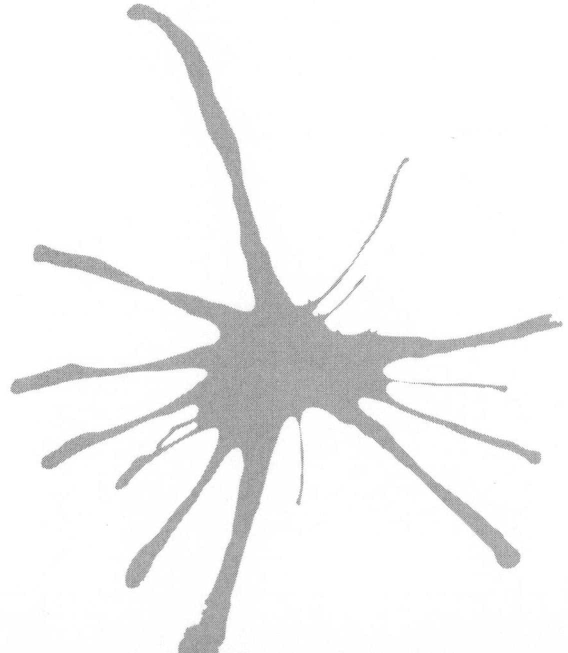

YOU MUST CHOOSE!

WOULD YOU RATHER...BE CAUGHT BY ALIENS AND PLACED IN AN ALIEN ZOO

OR BE USED FOR ALIEN SCIENTIFIC RESEARCH?

Would you rather...

accidentally wet the bed when sleeping over at someone else's house

OR

clog their toilet?

Would you rather...

eat all the flies off a piece of fly paper

OR

take 20 licks of a snot pop?

Would you rather...

no matter what, always have a wet spot on the front of your pants

OR

always have a milk mustache?

Would you rather...

share your room with 30 bats

OR

30 rats?

Would you rather...

have your house's running water replaced with pickle juice

OR

have your doorknobs replaced with living tortoise heads?

Would you rather...

drink a bottle of hot sauce

OR

pour the contents of a pepper shaker up your nose?

Would you rather...

have to make your home at the city dump landfill

OR

in a horse stable?

Would you rather...

brush your teeth with blended broccoli toothpaste

OR

use a glass of warm sweat as mouthwash?

YOU MUST CHOOSE!

Not fully grossed out yet?

Still wishing for more weirdness?

Look for these other *Would You Rather...?* books featuring hundreds of deranged dilemmas.

www.sevenfooterpress.com